EXPLORING WORLD HISTORY
QUIZ AND EXAM BOOK

Exploring World History Quiz and Exam Book
ISBN: 978-1-60999-072-5

Pictured on the cover: "The Antiquary" by Eva A. Withrow, etching by Eugene James Tily, courtesy Library of Congress

Printed in the United States of America

Notgrass Company
975 Roaring River Rd.
Gainesboro, TN 38562

1-800-211-8793
www.notgrass.com

Unit 5 Quiz

_____ 1. The Israelites were enslaved by Pharaoh because:
      a. they were good workers
      b. he felt threatened by them
      c. he was afraid they would leave
      d. he was afraid they would go on strike

_____ 2. How long did the Israelites have to wander in the desert?
      a. one year
      b. five years
      c. twenty-five years
      d. forty years

_____ 3. Who became the leader of the Israelites after Moses died?
      a. Joshua
      b. Aaron
      c. Levi
      d. Pharaoh

_____ 4. What date is the best estimate for the year of the Exodus?
      a. 7000 BC
      b. 5065 BC
      c. 1445 BC
      d. 450 BC

_____ 5. What does the Passover commemorate?
      a. God's deliverance
      b. Moses' appointment
      c. Aaron's priesthood
      d. Joshua's victories

_____ 6. From what tribe was Moses?
      a. Manasseh
      b. Reuben
      c. Judah
      d. Levi

_____ 7. Where did God speak to Moses from a burning bush?
      a. Mt. Gerizim
      b. Jerusalem
      c. Mt. Sinai
      d. Nile River

_____ 8. Why did Elimelech take his family to Moab?
      a. because of a famine in Israel
      b. to find wives for his sons
      c. because land was cheaper there
      d. to become governor

_____ 9. Boaz fulfilled for Ruth the role of:
      a. adoptive father
      b. kinsman redeemer
      c. master and owner
      d. priest and prophet

_____ 10. Who was Ruth's great-grandson?
      a. Moses
      b. Jesse
      c. Obed
      d. David

First History Exam (Units 1-5)

1. What nation did God call to Himself and designate as His chosen people?

_____

2. In what modern-day country is the Garden of Eden thought to have existed?

_____

3. Whom did God curse after the first sin in the Garden of Eden?

_____

4. What stone did Napoleon's troops discover in 1799?

_____

5. What kind of religious family background did Abraham have?

_____

6. What special feast commemorates God's deliverance of Israel in Egypt?

_____

7. To what land did Elimelech take his family?

_____

8. Boaz fulfilled for Ruth the role of what?

_____

exam continued on the next page

Matching.

_____ 9. He built a city and named it after his son.

_____ 10. He walked with God.

_____ 11. He was the originator of musical instruments.

_____ 12. He was the third named child born to Adam and Eve.

_____ 13. He was Noah's son and Abraham's anscestor.

_____ 14. He lived 969 years.

_____ 15. He ruled in Mesopotamia.

_____ 16. He was Abraham's father.

_____ 17. He was Abraham's nephew.

_____ 18. He was the father of Moses.

_____ 19. He was the father-in-law of Moses.

_____ 20. He was the son of Boaz.

a. Jubal

b. Hammurabi

c. Terah

d. Cain

e. Lot

f. Enoch

g. Amram

h. Obed

i. Methuselah

j. Reuel

k. Seth

l. Shem

First English Exam (Units 1-5)

1. "Ko Nga Tama a Rangi" bears similarities to what Biblical account?

_____

2. "Ko Nga Tama a Rangi" is a story from what country? _____

3. The story of Gajara, Dumbi, and Ngadja comes from what people group in what country?

_____

4. What is significant about the animals mentioned in the story about Gajara?

_____

5. What is the meaning of the Hebrew word *Dayenu*? _____

6. When is "Dayenu" typically sung? _____

7. What story is expressed in "Dayenu"?

_____

8. Who wrote *The Cat of Bubastes*? _____

9. What is the name of Chebron's sister? _____

10. Tell who Ameres is and describe his faith.

_____

_____

_____

_____

_____

Bible exam on the next page

First Bible Exam (Units 1-5)

1. Define eternity.

_____

_____

_____

_____

_____

2. What religion became a major force in Mesopotamia in the 7th century?

_____

3. What five books are included in the Pentateuch?

_____

_____

4. Why are the sacrifices described in the Law of Moses no longer necessary?

_____

_____

_____

5. Write a paragraph describing the life of Joseph.

_____

_____

_____

_____

_____

_____

_____

Unit 6 Quiz

_____ 1. Whose advice did Rehoboam heed?
      a. his elders   c. his young counselors
      b. his wives   d. his children

_____ 2. What king allowed the Jews to return to their homeland?
      a. Nebuchadnezzar   c. Darius
      b. Nehemiah   d. Cyrus

_____ 3. Goliath was a warrior of the:
      a. Hittites   c. Philistines
      b. Canaanites   d. Moabites

_____ 4. The Phoenicians were known for:
      a. the Hanging Gardens   c. being fierce warriors
      b. seafaring and trading   d. moneychanging

_____ 5. What was the name of the Phoenician port known for its trade in papyrus?
      a. Byblos   c. Biblica
      b. Biblion   d. Bylicus

_____ 6. In what nation was the city of Ninevah?
      a. Assyria   c. Israel
      b. Phoenicia   d. Babylon

_____ 7. Who oversaw the construction of the temple in Jerusalem?
      a. Samuel   c. David
      b. Saul   d. Solomon

_____ 8. Who asked God to give him an understanding heart?
      a. Jonathan   c. Saul
      b. Solomon   d. Jesse

_____ 9. Which book of the Bible listed below did Solomon write?
      a. Psalms   c. Ecclesiastes
      b. Job   d. 1 Kings

_____ 10. What led Solomon astray from the Lord?
      a. his wealth   c. his alliance with Hiram of Tyre
      b. his foreign wives   d. his jealousy of David

Unit 7 Quiz

Write a T if the statement is true and an F if the statement is false. If the statement is false, write a true version of the statement below it.

_____ 1. A satrap in the Persian empire was a governor of a province.

_____

_____

_____ 2. The Royal Road was the centerpiece of the Persian road system.

_____

_____

_____ 3. The Persian Empire fell in 330 BC to Julius Caesar.

_____

_____

_____ 4. Zoroastrianism sought to eliminate polytheism.

_____

_____

_____ 5. Augustine was a Christian before he became a Manichaean.

_____

_____

_____ 6. The Bible describes Cyrus as the Lord's anointed.

_____

_____

_____ 7. The records of Cyrus were found on a cylinder.

_____

_____ 8. Shadrach, Meshach, and Abed-nego refused to worship the golden image.

_____

_____

_____ 9. Daniel interpreted handwriting on the gate.

_____

_____

_____ 10. Daniel was thrown into a lion's den because he would not worship King Cyrus.

_____

_____

Unit 8 Quiz

_____ 1. Along what river did an early civilization emerge in India?
     a. Ganges   c. Mekong
     b. Tigris   d. Indus

_____ 2. What is the name given to the group of people who migrated out of the region north of the Caucus Mountains and between the Black and Caspian Seas?
     a. Chinese   c. Mongolian
     b. Indo-European   d. Celts

_____ 3. Chung Kuo means:
     a. Great Society   c. Leading Nation
     b. Middle Kingdom   d. Heaven on Earth

_____ 4. A famous philosopher of ancient China was:
     a. Confucius   c. Han
     b. Chungkao   d. Ch'in

_____ 5. What civilization had a capital located near present-day Mexico City?
     a. Incas   c. Druids
     b. Aztecs   d. Kush

_____ 6. Taoism encouraged much:
     a. contemplation   c. violence
     b. action   d. study

_____ 7. What two ancient nations became Ethiopia?
     a. Kush and Egypt   c. Kush and Axum
     b. Axum and Persia   d. Egypt and Put

_____ 8. The Druids were a religious cult of what people group?
     a. Angles   c. Vikings
     b. Celts   d. Greeks

_____ 9. What civilization inhabited the area that is now the country of Peru?
     a. Inca   c. Indo-Europeans
     b. Aztec   d. Axum

_____ 10. What conquering nation founded the town of Londinium in England?
     a. Celts   c. Vikings
     b. Angles   d. Romans

Unit 9 Quiz

_____ 1. Who united the Greek cities before he was assassinated in 336 BC?

_____ 2. What kind of Greek was used to write the New Testament?

_____ 3. Who wrote *The Iliad* and *The Odyssey*?

_____ 4. What Greek practitioner of medicine believed that diseases have natural causes?

_____ 5. Who was put to death for "corrupting the youth and introducing false beliefs"?

_____ 6. Who capitalized on a Greek military victory over Persia to gain political influence in Athens?

_____ 7. To what goddess was the Parthenon dedicated?

_____ 8. Euclid, Thales, and what other man are remembered for studying geometry?

_____ 9. A rivalry between Athens and what other city-state led to the Peloponnesian War?

_____ 10. What ancient Greek writer wrote an historical account of the Persian War based on his investigation of what really happened?

a. Koine

b. Hippocrates

c. Sparta

d. Pericles

e. Athena

f. Herodotus

g. Philip of Macedonia

h. Pythagoras

i. Homer

j. Socrates

Unit 10 Quiz

_____ 1. Who authored the *Aeneid*?
    a. Romulus
    b. Virgil
    c. Tiberius
    d. Homer

_____ 2. What nation was Rome's adversary in the Punic Wars?
    a. Carthage
    b. Greece
    c. Israel
    d. Punisia

_____ 3. What does the title "Augustus" mean?
    a. Powerful One
    b. Humble One
    c. Exalted One
    d. Remembered One

_____ 4. What language is the basis for many European languages today?
    a. Roman
    b. Latin
    c. German
    d. Greek

_____ 5. Who oversaw the law courts of the Roman republic?
    a. res publia
    b. res juria
    c. praetor
    d. pontius

_____ 6. What is the complete codification of Roman laws, legal principles, and commentaries often called?
    a. Code of Hammurabi
    b. Code of Conduct
    c. Code of Caesar
    d. Justinian Code

_____ 7. What city was buried by a volcanic eruption in 79 AD?
    a. Pompeii
    b. Rome
    c. Vesuvius
    d. Minorca

_____ 8. What structure was a temple to all gods?
    a. Panhellas
    b. Pantheon
    c. Pancreatica
    d. Panhandlia

_____ 9. A key element of Roman construction was the:
    a. arch
    b. basement
    c. stairway
    d. steeple

_____ 10. From what culture did Epicureanism and Stoicism originate?
    a. Roman
    b. Lebanese
    c. Greek
    d. Jewish

Second History Exam (Units 6-10)

1. What Israelite king heeded the advice of his young counselors instead of his elders?

_____

2. What king allowed the Jews who were in captivity to return to their homeland?

_____

3. Who oversaw the construction of the temple in Jerusalem? _____

4. What led Solomon astray from the Lord? _____

5. What was the centerpiece of the Persian road system? _____

6. To whom did the Persian Empire fall in 330 BC? _____

7. After spending nine years as a Manichaean, what did Augustine become?

_____

8. The records of which Persian ruler were found written on a cylinder?

_____

9. Who interpreted handwriting on a wall at a banquet of Belshazzar?

_____

10. The Indo-European tribes migrated out of the region north of the Caucus Mountains and between what two bodies of water?

_____

11. What term did the Chinese use for themselves from antiquity?

_____

exam continued on the next page

12. What ancient Chinese philosophy encouraged little doing and much contemplation?

_____

13. What civilization had a capital located near present-day Mexico City?

_____

14. Who is the author of *The Illiad* and *The Odyssey*?

_____

15. What are Euclid, Thales, and Pythagoras remembered for studying?

_____

16. A rivalry between Athens and Sparta led to what war?

_____

17. What were the opposing sides in the Punic Wars?

_____

18. What language is the basis for many European languages today?

_____

19. What natural disaster hit Pompeii in 79 AD?

_____

20. What Roman structure was a temple to all gods?

_____

Second English Exam (Units 6-10)

_____ 1. *The Art of War* is from what country?
   a. England
   b. China
   c. Germany
   d. Japan

_____ 2. *The Art of War* is usually dated:
   a. before the time of Christ
   b. during the late Middle Ages
   c. from World War II
   d. during Communist control

_____ 3. If an army is outnumbered, *The Art of War* recommends that it:
   a. surrender
   b. negotiate
   c. evade or withdraw
   d. disband

_____ 4. The best position in a battle is:
   a. in front of water
   b. to the rear of water
   c. downhill from the enemy
   d. uphill from the enemy

_____ 5. A good way for an army commander to understand the position and strength of the enemy is:
   a. studying smoke from campfires
   b. following their horses and wagons
   c. using spies to gain information
   d. studying the enemy's military history

_____ 6. The play *Julius Caesar* is about:
   a. ambition
   b. historical accuracy
   c. the Greek gods
   d. Caesar's campaign to Britain

_____ 7. What did the soothsayer say to Caesar?
   a. "Lend me your ears."
   b. "Veni, vidi, vici."
   c. "Brutus is an honorable man."
   d. "Beware the Ides of March."

_____ 8. The conspirators thought that after the assassination of Caesar, the people would:
   a. make one of them king.
   b. demand reform in government.
   c. let them decide who would rule Rome.
   d. be glad to be relieved of a tyrant.

_____ 9. Brutus said that he participated in the assassination of Caesar because:
   a. he was overcome with envy.
   b. he loved Rome more.
   c. he wanted Antony to be king.
   d. he wanted to establish a democracy.

_____ 10. How much money did Caesar leave to the people of Rome?
   a. 75 drachmas to be divided evenly
   b. 75 drachmas each
   c. 100 drachmas for each family
   d. 50 drachmas each

exam continued on the next page

Match each character from Julius Caesar *on the left to the correct description on the right.*

_____ 11. Brutus

_____ 12. Julius Caesar

_____ 13. Antony

_____ 14. Cassius

_____ 15. Octavius

_____ 16. Casca

_____ 17. Calpurnia

_____ 18. Portia

_____ 19. Cicero

_____ 20. Decius

a. friend of Caesar who delivers tearful funeral oration

b. warns Caesar about going to the Senate on the Ides of March

c. Caesar's adopted son and successor

d. extremely loyal to the Republic and against a dictatorship

e. talented general envious of Caesar's fame

f. great Roman general and senator

g. a Roman senator and talented orator

h. convinces Caesar that he will not be in danger at the Senate

i. wife of Brutus

j. public figure who believes Caesar is lulling the populace by turning down the crown

Second Bible Exam (Units 6-10)

_____ 1. What term means "spokesman for God"?
    a. angel   c. priest
    b. prophet   d. cherub

_____ 2. Which prophet was a shepherd and fig grower?
    a. Amos   c. Jeremiah
    b. Jonah   d. Micah

_____ 3. What was significant about the law of the Medes and Persians?
    a. It changed often.   c. It could not be changed.
    b. It became the basis for American law.   d. It influenced the Law of Moses.

_____ 4. Who was given Haman's property after Haman was executed?
    a. Ahasuerus   c. Esther
    b. Haman's sons   d. Haman's wife

_____ 5. What Jewish feast commemorates the Lord's deliverance of the Jews from Haman?
    a. Purim   c. Hannukah
    b. Passover   d. Yom Kippur

_____ 6. What did God use to illustrate to Jonah the injustice of his resentment to the Ninevites' repentance?
    a. a big fish   c. fire and brimstone
    b. a plant and a worm   d. a quiet stream

_____ 7. Who is the first recorded person to take the gospel to Europe?
    a. Peter   c. Paul
    b. James   d. Philip

_____ 8. In which city did an altar stand dedicated "To an unknown god"?
    a. Athens   c. Ephesus
    b. Corinth   d. Alexandria

_____ 9. To be a part of the kingdom of God, one must be like what?
    a. a king   c. a teacher
    b. an emperor   d. a child

_____ 10. Which of the following is true about the kingdom of God?
    a. It is not of this world.   c. It began as a mustard seed.
    b. It will not pass away.   d. All of the above.

Unit 11 Quiz

Write a T if the statement is true and an F if the statement is false. If the statement is false, write a true version of the statement below it.

_____ 1. Luke addressed his book to Theophilus.

_____

_____ 2. Luke was a fisherman.

_____

_____ 3. The Sadducees were a group of Jews who denied the resurrection.

_____

_____ 4. The Zealots were Jews who devoted themselves to the cause of Roman unification.

_____

_____ 5. The 5,000 men described in John 6 wanted to make Jesus their carpenter.

_____

_____ 6. The Samaritans were descendants of people of the Northern Kingdom and Assyrians.

_____

_____ 7. Jews generally disliked the tax collectors.

_____

_____ 8. Jesus compared the kingdom of God to an apple seed.

_____

_____ 9. Jesus slept all night before he chose the twelve apostles.

_____

_____ 10. Luke emphasizes the need for repentance.

_____

Unit 12 Quiz

_____ 1. About how many people responded to Peter's first proclamation of the gospel?
  a. 3
  b. 30
  c. 300
  d. 3,000

_____ 2. Who was God's chosen instrument to take the message of Jesus to the Gentiles?
  a. Peter
  b. Andrew
  c. Paul
  d. Silas

_____ 3. The conversion of Cornelius was significant because:
  a. Cornelius financed Paul's missionary work.
  b. God told Cornelius directly from heaven how to be saved.
  c. It was Peter's first evangelistic sermon.
  d. Gentiles were baptized and thus brought into the fellowship of Christians.

_____ 4. What happened while Peter was speaking to Cornelius and his household?
  a. Cornelius began prophesying.
  b. The Holy Spirit came on all who heard the message.
  c. Jews burst in and had Peter arrested.
  d. Peter had a vision of Jesus.

_____ 5. By what famous teacher was Paul taught?
  a. Hillel
  b. Shammai
  c. Ananias
  d. Gamaliel

_____ 6. To what city was Paul going when he was "arrested" by Jesus?
  a. Jerusalem
  b. Antioch
  c. Damascus
  d. Philippi

_____ 7. To whom did Paul appeal his case?
  a. Caesar
  b. Peter
  c. Agrippa
  d. Nero

_____ 8. How did Paul obtain his Roman citizenship?
  a. with a large amount of money
  b. by bargaining
  c. by birth
  d. with trickery

_____ 9. What two groups opposed each other when Paul spoke to the Council?
  a. Zealots and Romans
  b. Sadducees and Pharisees
  c. Christians and Jews
  d. poor and wealthy

_____ 10. What aberrant Jewish practices are described in Acts?
  a. sorcery and magic
  b. eating pork and camel meat
  c. listening to music backwards
  d. proselytizing Gentiles

Unit 13 Quiz

_____ 1. He divided the Roman Empire into eastern and western sections.

a. Claudius

_____ 2. He issued the Edict of Milan, which declared tolerance for Christianity throughout the Roman Empire.

b. Theodosius I

_____ 3. He was a leader of the Hun people.

c. Diocletian

_____ 4. He ordered that all Jews leave Rome.

d. Peter

_____ 5. He wrote in defense of the Christian faith.

e. Odoacer

_____ 6. He declared Rome to be a Christian state in 381.

f. Constantine

_____ 7. He was declared to have been the first bishop of Rome many years after his death.

g. Athenasius

_____ 8. He produced a Latin translation of the Bible called the Vulgate.

h. Attila

_____ 9. He declared himself king of Rome in 476.

i. Jerome

_____ 10. He countered the claim of Arius stating that Christ's relationship with God was always the same.

j. Justin

Unit 14 Quiz

_____ 1. The millennium between the fall of Rome and the Italian Renaissance has been called:
- a. The Early Ages
- b. The Terrible Ages
- c. The Dark Ages
- d. The Late Ages

_____ 2. What was the primary influence during the Middle Ages?
- a. science
- b. religion
- c. art
- d. agriculture

_____ 3. What group from Scandinavia acquired Normandy in 911?
- a. Romans
- b. Huns
- c. Norsemen
- d. Mongols

_____ 4. What were the common Arab religious beliefs before Mohammed?
- a. usually either Jewish or Christian
- b. many gods and spiritual beings
- c. ideas based on John the Baptist
- d. deification of the Queen of Sheba

_____ 5. What significant event happened in 622 AD?
- a. Mohammed got married.
- b. Mohammed began conquering Europe
- c. Islam divided into Shi'ites and Sunnis.
- d. Mohammed fled from Mecca to Medina.

_____ 6. What is the term for an Islamic holy war?
- a. Jihad
- b. Crusade
- c. Mohammed's Battle
- d. Qur'an

_____ 7. What invaders did Alfred face as a youth?
- a. Romans
- b. Saxons
- c. Danes or Vikings
- d. All of the above

_____ 8. What were Alfred's religious views?
- a. He was a Muslim.
- b. He was devoted to the Lord.
- c. He worshipped many gods.
- d. He was an atheist.

_____ 9. Where did the Vikings come from?
- a. Sweden
- b. Norway
- c. Denmark
- d. All of the above

_____ 10. How far west did the Vikings explore?
- a. Canada
- b. Greenland
- c. Iceland
- d. England

Unit 15 Quiz

_____ 1. What country did William, Duke of Normandy invade and conquer in 1066?
   a. France
   b. Germany
   c. Scotland
   d. England

_____ 2. In what war did Joan of Arc lead the armies of France?
   a. the Thirty Years War
   b. the Hundred Years War
   c. the Franco-German War
   d. the French and Italian War

_____ 3. What was the significance of the capture of Grenada in 1492?
   a. It was the first victory of its kind.
   b. It was the shortest battle in history.
   c. It was the last Muslim outpost in Spain.
   d. It was the last Christian outpost in Spain.

_____ 4. What was a fealty?
   a. an oath of loyalty
   b. a tract of land
   c. a gift to the church
   d. a tower in a castle

_____ 5. What was the main objective of the First Crusade?
   a. to evangelize the Muslims
   b. to build a Christian state in Egypt
   c. to evangelize Europe
   d. to liberate Palestine from the Muslims

_____ 6. What English king led the Third Crusade?
   a. John
   b. Arthur
   c. Richard I, the Lionhearted
   d. Alfred the Great

_____ 7. Where was Thomas Aquinas born?
   a. France
   b. Italy
   c. Spain
   d. England

_____ 8. For what work is Thomas Aquinas best known?
   a. _Summa Theologica_
   b. _The Odyssey_
   c. _Pange Lingua_
   d. _Corporis Mysterium_

_____ 9. Thomas Aquinas believed that what two things compliment each other?
   a. faith and doubt
   b. Christianity and paganism
   c. reason and revelation
   d. science and magic

_____ 10. Roger Bacon encouraged the pursuit of knowledge by:
   a. seeking divine revelation
   b. studying ancient scholars
   c. experimentation and observation
   d. discussion with Muslims

Third History Exam (Units 11-15)

1. What was the profession of the author of the books of Luke and Acts?

   _____

2. What Jewish group did not believe in the resurrection?

   _____

3. What people group were descendants of the Northern Kingdom of Israel and Assyrians?

   _____

4. Jews who devoted themselves to the cause of liberation from Rome were known as what?

   _____

5. To what was Jesus referring when He told His disciples that they would be "clothed with power from on high"?

   _____

6. What man, along with his household, was the first Gentile to be baptized and come into fellowship with Jewish Christians?

   _____

7. In what city was the apostle Paul born? _____

8. To whom did Paul appeal his case? _____

9. Who issued the Edict of Milan? _____

10. What of significance to the Jews was destroyed in 70 AD? _____

11. Into what language did Jerome translate the Bible? _____

12. Who ordered that all Jews leave Rome? _____

exam continued on the next page

13. What was the primary influence on society during the Middle Ages?

_____

14. What is the name of the book of Mohammed's sayings?

_____

15. What son of Ethelwulf of Wessex became king of England in the late 800s?

_____

16. How far west did the Vikings explore?

_____

17. In what year did William, Duke of Normandy, invade and conquer England?

_____

18. Who was the female leader of the armies of France during the Hundred Years War?

_____

19. What endeavors were undertaken in an attempt to liberate Palestine from the Muslims beginning in 1095?

_____

20. Who is the author of *Summa Theologica*?

_____

Third English Exam (Units 11-15)

1. "The Watchman" is a fictional account of what Biblical event?

_____

2. What function did the narrator of "The Watchman" play?

_____

3. In "The Watchman," what did Maximus see that changed the desires of his heart?

_____

4. "A Death in the Desert" is written from the perspective of whom? _____

5. What did the main character in "A Death in the Desert" go around the world saying?

_____

6. The main character in "A Death in the Desert" said that he saw Jesus doing what?

_____

7. "Eirik the Red's Saga" is set primarily in what country?

_____

8. The story of Lonopuha is set in what place? _____

9. Who is the author of *The Imitation of Christ*? _____

10. *Everyman* is a morality play from what time period? _____

11. Write a one-paragraph synopsis of *Everyman*.

_____

_____

_____

_____

_____

_____

_____

_____

Bible exam on the next page

Third Bible Exam (Units 11-15)

_____ 1. What does the name "Jerusalem" mean?
      a. City of Hostility   c. City of David
      b. City of Peace   d. City of Light

_____ 2. What king made Jerusalem the capital of the nation of Israel?
      a. Saul   c. Solomon
      b. David   d. Josiah

_____ 3. What nation controlled Palestine at the time of the birth of Christ?
      a. Rome   c. Persia
      b. Greece   d. Babylon

_____ 4. What is a major theme repeated in the book of Philippians?
      a. generosity   c. resurrection
      b. heaven   d. attitude

_____ 5. In Philippians Paul appeals to the Christians in Philippi to have the _____ of Christ.
      a. eyes   c. humility
      b. mind   d. ears

_____ 6. To what teaching was the church of the first century devoted?
      a. gnostic   c. rabbinical
      b. apostles'   d. Augustinian

_____ 7. In the third and fourth centuries, what practice attempted to answer the problem of worldliness in the church and encouraged deep devotion to God?
      a. Monasticism   c. becoming a Zealot
      b. Phariseeism   d. purchasing indulgences

_____ 8. Who became an ordained bishop and went to the country where he had formerly been a slave to tell people about Jesus?
      a. Ethelred   c. Patrick
      b. Cyril   d. Methodius

_____ 9. What evangelist converted Ethelbert, the Saxon king of England, to Christianity?
      a. Augustine   c. Constantine
      b. Frederick   d. Methodius

_____ 10. What is pre-evangelism?
      a. pointing people away from the Bible
      b. helping a person become willing to be taught about Christ
      c. talking about the cross but not about the resurrection
      d. becoming a monastic

Unit 16 Quiz

_____ 1. Became a major power in 1299

_____ 2. A leading influence in the Renaissance

_____ 3. Professional soldiers hired out as mercenary police

_____ 4. Inventor of moveable type

_____ 5. Creator of the _Mona Lisa_

_____ 6. Creator of the seventeen-foot-tall _David_

_____ 7. An artist of the Baroque period

_____ 8. Began composing at the age of five

_____ 9. Composed music after going deaf

_____ 10. Prominent Italian banking family

a. condottieri

b. Michelangelo

c. Bach

d. Beethoven

e. Ottoman Empire

f. Mozart

g. Gutenberg

h. da Vinci

i. Italy

j. Medici

Unit 17 Quiz

_____ 1. Releasing a soul from purgatory in exchange for a contribution was called:
    a. heresy
    b. perambulation
    c. institutio
    d. an indulgence

_____ 2. Where did Martin Luther nail his Ninety-Five Theses?
    a. St. Peter's Basilica in Rome
    b. a church door in Wittenberg
    c. a gate in London
    d. a church pulpit in Berlin

_____ 3. Who was excommunicated from the church because he divorced his wife and married again without receiving an annulment from the pope?
    a. Prince John
    b. King Alfred
    c. Henry VIII
    d. Richard I

_____ 4. John Calvin was a prominent citizen of what city?
    a. Geneva
    b. Rome
    c. London
    d. Paris

_____ 5. _Institutes of the Christian Religion_ was:
    a. a Catholic scholarship society
    b. Calvin's defense of Michael Servetus
    c. Luther's protest against the pope
    d. Calvin's best-known work of theology

_____ 6. What did the Anabaptists emphasize as the sign of the "true church"?
    a. regular attendance to church meetings
    b. infant baptism
    c. holy lifestyle
    d. daily Bible reading

_____ 7. What did Aldred translate into Anglo-Saxon in the 900s?
    a. the Old Testament
    b. the entire Bible
    c. the gospels
    d. Psalms

_____ 8. Who was put to death for translating the Bible into English?
    a. Jerome
    b. William Tyndale
    c. Patrick
    d. John Wycliffe

_____ 9. Miles Coverdale oversaw the translation of the:
    a. Great Bible
    b. Geneva Bible
    c. Gutenberg Bible
    d. American Standard Bible

_____ 10. Who authorized an English translation of the Bible in 1611?
    a. John Calvin
    b. Menno Simons
    c. Jerome
    d. King James I

Unit 18 Quiz

_____ 1. Marco Polo:
   a. helped expand European borders
   b. opposed Columbus' plans
   c. was an advisor to the pope
   d. proposed sailing north to reach Asia

_____ 2. What were the two predominant motivations for English colonial settlements?
   a. democracy and literacy
   b. defeat of the Spanish and discovery of gold
   c. economic gain and religious freedom
   d. trade with Asia and establishment of a new monarchy

_____ 3. What development in the Middle East prompted Europeans to seek a water route to Asia?
   a. taxes imposed by Arab traders
   b. the defeat of the Crusaders
   c. the Ottoman defeat of Byzantium
   d. Columbus' discovery of a new world

_____ 4. What country rejected Columbus' proposal first?
   a. Italy
   b. Portugal
   c. England
   d. France

_____ 5. Who elected Charles V to become Holy Roman Emperor in 1516?
   a. German princes
   b. European kings
   c. Roman church leaders
   d. English scholars

_____ 6. What happened in 1588 that changed the balance of power in Europe?
   a. the Thirty Years War
   b. the Spanish defeat of the Dutch
   c. England's defeat of the Spanish Armada
   d. the War of the Roses in England

_____ 7. In the conflict between Spain and England:
   a. religion played no part
   b. England wanted to put a Protestant on the Spanish throne
   c. England was becoming mostly Catholic
   d. one issue was Spain's Catholicism and England's Protestantism

_____ 8. What nickname was given to the change in the weather that took place during the battle between the Spanish Armada and the English Navy?
   a. Catholic Storm
   b. Protestant Wind
   c. English Wave
   d. Spanish Storm

_____ 9. What term was used to describe Muslims who had converted to Christianity?
   a. Moriscoes
   b. Anabaptists
   c. Islamists
   d. Inquisitors

_____ 10. What piece of furniture was at one time rare in European homes and came to be seen as a symbol of wealth and power, reserved for the head of the family or a guest?
   a. bed
   b. footstool
   c. couch
   d. chair

Unit 19 Quiz

Write a T if the statement is true and an F if the statement is false. If the statement is false, write a true version of the statement below it.

_____ 1. The Enlightenment is seen as beginning with Newton's *Pricipia Mathematica*.

_____

_____

_____ 2. The Enlightenment is seen as ending with the American Revolution.

_____

_____

_____ 3. Galileo discussed ideas with German astronomer Johannes Kepler.

_____

_____

_____ 4. Galileo was denounced for adhering to the theories of Copernicus.

_____

_____

_____ 5. The Inquisition banned Galileo's book and imprisoned him.

_____

_____ 6. Isaac Newton developed algebra.

_____

_____ 7. Newton discussed gravitation in his book *Mathematical Principles of Natural Philosophy*.

_____

_____

_____ 8. Newton was prideful about his accomplishments.

_____

_____

_____ 9. Newton became the first scientist to be married in Westminster Abbey.

_____

_____

_____ 10. Isaac Singer successfully marketed sewing machines in the 1850s.

_____

_____

Unit 20 Quiz

_____ 1. The form of government in which a monarch has complete power is called:
    a. Democracy   c. Absolutism
    b. Republic   d. Communism

_____ 2. What significant event took place in England in 1642?
    a. famine   c. civil war
    b. mass riots   d. plague

_____ 3. Who was England's reigning monarch during the American Revolution?
    a. George III   c. Richard I
    b. Elizabeth I   d. Charles I

_____ 4. What term is used to describe the French Calvinist Protestants who were at odds with the Catholics during the 1500s?
    a. Huguenots   c. Mennonites
    b. Puritans   d. Separatists

_____ 5. Who believed he was as important to France as the sun is to the world?
    a. Cardinal Richelieu   c. John Locke
    b. Louis XIV   d. Philip II

_____ 6. What leader was behind the Reign of Terror?
    a. Robert Turgot   c. Marie Antoinette
    b. de Montesquieu   d. Robespierre

_____ 7. Who developed the philosophical idea of Empiricism?
    a. Louis XVI   c. John Locke
    b. Isaac Newton   d. Rousseau

_____ 8. In John Locke's view, who had ultimate sovereignty in government?
    a. the people   c. the king
    b. the elected legislature   d. the elected head of state

_____ 9. When teaching children about the physical world, Locke believed:
    a. they should learn it separately from Bible knowledge
    b. they should learn Bible knowledge first
    c. they should not learn about the physical world
    d. they should not learn about the Bible in school

_____ 10. Who introduced coffee in Europe in 1615?
    a. Marco Polo   c. French nobility
    b. Chinese philosophers   d. Venetian merchants

Fourth History Exam (Units 16-20)

_____ 1. Inventor of moveable type

_____ 2. Painter, sculptor, engineer, architect, and musician

_____ 3. Prominent Italian banking family

_____ 4. Author of the Ninety-Five Theses

_____ 5. Prominent citizen of Geneva

_____ 6. Put to death for translating the Bible into English

_____ 7. Overseer of the translation known as the Great Bible

_____ 8. Oxford professor and Bible translator

_____ 9. Italian explorer who represented a Medici bank

_____ 10. Elected to become Holy Roman Emperor in 1516

_____ 11. Native of Genoa, Italy

_____ 12. English dynasty of Henry VIII

_____ 13. Author of *Principia Mathematica*

_____ 14. German astronomer

_____ 15. Imprisoned by the Inquisition

_____ 16. King of England during the American Revolution

_____ 17. Believed he was as important as the sun

_____ 18. Leader behind the Reign of Terror

_____ 19. Compared the human mind at birth to a blank slate

_____ 20. Author of America's Declaration of Independence

a. Medici

b. John Wycliffe

c. Tudor

d. Amerigo Vespucci

e. Isaac Newton

f. Louis XIV

g. Johannes Kepler

h. Robespierre

i. Gutenberg

j. George III

k. Thomas Jefferson

l. da Vinci

m. William Tyndale

n. Martin Luther

o. Christopher Columbus

p. John Calvin

q. Galileo

r. Charles V

s. Miles Coverdale

t. John Locke

Fourth English Exam (Units 16-20)

Fill in the blank.

1. *The Praise of Folly* was written by _____ in 1509.

2. In *Don Quixote,* the main character sought to become a _____.

3. Martin Luther posted his Ninety-Five _____ on a church door in Wittenberg.

4. Luther's translation of the Bible had an impact on the _____ language.

5. The practice of declaring a loved one released from purgatory in exchange for a donation to the church is called the selling of _____.

6. When Martin Luther was caught in a storm, he decided to become a _____.

7. Luther's reforms were able to take hold in part because of the support of German

   _____.

8. John Calvin wrote *Institutes of the* _____ _____ in 1545.

9. *Opticks* tells of Isaac Newton's experiments with _____.

10. John Locke was the author of *Two Treatises of* _____.

11. The author of *A Tale of Two Cities* is _____ _____.

12. *A Tale of Two Cities* is set during the _____ _____.

13. At the beginning of the book, _____ _____ was recalled to life.

14. Madame Defarge was always _____.

15. What service did Sydney Carton render to Charles Darnay at the end of the book?

_____

Fourth Bible Exam (Units 16-20)

_____ 1. Who asked, "What must I do to be saved?"
     a. Paul
     b. the Philippian jailer
     c. the lame man at the temple
     d. Silas

_____ 2. According to Ephesians 2:3, what is a person prior to salvation?
     a. worthless
     b. an object of wrath
     c. a narrow gate
     d. a stumbling block

_____ 3. How many Israelite men were sent to spy out the land of Canaan?
     a. 2
     b. 10
     c. 12
     d. 21

_____ 4. What two spies believed the Lord would bring the Israelites into Canaan?
     a. Moses and Aaron
     b. Othniel and Ehud
     c. Moses and Joshua
     d. Joshua and Caleb

_____ 5. What motivated the Israelites to attack Canaan without the Lord's help?
     a. fear
     b. lack of knowledge
     c. pride
     d. fogetfulness

_____ 6. Who described himself as being fearfully and wonderfully made?
     a. David
     b. Moses
     c. Joseph
     d. Abraham

_____ 7. In what should Christians boast?
     a. their salvation
     b. their freedom
     c. the will of God
     d. the cross of Christ

_____ 8. Paul told the Christians in Galatia that they were heirs of what?
     a. earthly riches
     b. healthy church relationships
     c. God's promise of justification
     d. the power of Jesus

exam continued on the next page

9. Describe the condition of someone you have known personally who was medically vulnerable.

_____

_____

_____

_____

_____

10. Write a paragraph expressing thankfulness for the political and spiritual freedoms you enjoy.

_____

_____

_____

_____

_____

_____

_____

Unit 21 Quiz

_____ 1. To what position was Napoleon elevated in 1802?
     a. First Citizen   c. First Director
     b. First Consul   d. First Frenchman

_____ 2. In what country did Napoleon meet defeat in 1812?
     a. England   c. Russia
     b. France   d. Spain

_____ 3. What meeting sorted out the post-Napoleon political issues of Europe?
     a. Congress of Mainz   c. Congress of Vienna
     b. Concordat of Paris   d. Estates-General

_____ 4. Who led France's Second Republic?
     a. Louis XVI   c. Count Cavillo
     b. Napoleon   d. Louis Blanc

_____ 5. What empire experienced several revolts in 1848?
     a. Serbian   c. German
     b. Ottoman   d. Austrian

_____ 6. What dynasty ruled Russia from 1613 to 1917?
     a. Marx   c. Romanov
     b. Orthodox   d. Nikolai

_____ 7. Who founded Young Italy in 1831?
     a. Houdini   c. Mazzini
     b. Cavour   d. Garibaldi

_____ 8. What two German states were most powerful by the mid-1700s?
     a. Austria and Saxony   c. Austria and Prussia
     b. Prussia and Berlin   d. Austria and Erfurt

_____ 9. The volunteer army organized in southern Italy by Giuseppe Garibaldi was called:
     a. Red Shirts   c. Black Belts
     b. Red Scarves   d. Blue Liberators

_____ 10. What term is used to describe elaborately decorated copies of Scripture?
     a. Illustrated   c. Mannerism
     b. Baroque   d. Illuminated

Unit 22 Quiz

Write a T if the statement is true and an F if the statement is false. If the statement is false, write a true version of the statement below it.

_____ 1. Two benefits of Britain's overseas empire were raw materials and new markets.

_____

_____

_____ 2. At the height of its empire, Russia controlled one-fifth of the world's land area.

_____

_____

_____ 3. Some gave up personal and economic freedom through the Industrial Revolution.

_____

_____

_____ 4. One million Irish died as a result of the potato famine.

_____

_____ 5. William Gladstone tried to get a law passed that would give India home rule.

_____

_____

_____ 6. The Republic of Ireland was formed in 1948.

_____

_____ 7. George Müller helped around 10,000 orphaned children.

_____

_____

_____ 8. George Müller often asked individuals to contribute to his work.

_____

_____

_____ 9. The first practical railroad engine was unveiled in England in 1829.

_____

_____

_____ 10. A suspension bridge connects England and France over the English Channel.

_____

_____

Unit 23 Quiz

_____ 1. The *Communist Manifesto* was written by whom?
    a. Karl Marx
    b. Friedrich Engels
    c. Karl Marx and Friedrich Engels
    d. Karl Marx and Sigmund Freud

_____ 2. What force did Marx believe determines events?
    a. economics
    b. religion
    c. agriculture
    d. critical thinking

_____ 3. Who wrote *On the Origin of Species*?
    a. Karl Marx
    b. Sigmund Freud
    c. Johannes Kepler
    d. Charles Darwin

_____ 4. What attempt to compare features in living things is sometimes used to support evolution?
    a. uniformitarianism
    b. comparative anatomy
    c. trigonomic bi-classification
    d. fossilization

_____ 5. Darwin admitted that a lack of what kind of evidence hurt his theory?
    a. fossil evidence
    b. mineral evidence
    c. eyewitness evidence
    d. Scriptural evidence

_____ 6. Sigmund Freud is considered a pioneer in what field?
    a. psychoanalysis
    b. brain surgery
    c. genetics
    d. sociology

_____ 7. How did Freud define the ego?
    a. physical desires
    b. sense of self
    c. awareness of the world
    d. awareness of our right and wrong

_____ 8. What did Freud believe to be the chief purpose of life?
    a. acquisition of wealth
    b. peacefulness
    c. happiness
    d. learning about the past

_____ 9. Who developed instrumentalism?
    a. Sigmund Freud
    b. Jean Piaget
    c. Friedrich Engels
    d. John Dewey

_____ 10. What does Proverbs say is the beginning of knowledge?
    a. learning to read
    b. understanding instruction
    c. the fear of the Lord
    d. a discerning heart

Unit 24 Quiz

_____ 1. What countries formed the Triple Alliance?
    a. England, the U.S., and Russia   c. Germany, Japan, and Italy
    b. France, Spain, and Russia   d. Germany, Austria-Hungary, and Italy

_____ 2. Who assassinated the Austrian Archduke Franz Ferdinand?
    a. a German civilian   c. a Hungarian monk
    b. a Serbian nationalist   d. an Italian politician

_____ 3. What kind of government came to power in Russia during World War I?
    a. Communist   c. Democracy
    b. Monarchy   d. Dictatorship

_____ 4. Where did Japan attack in 1941?
    a. Bay of Pigs   c. Pearl Harbor
    b. Berlin   d. Rome

_____ 5. What did the U.S. do through the Marshall Plan?
    a. helped Europe rebuild   c. established a new German government
    b. built new ships for Japan   d. sent returning soldiers to college

_____ 6. What was Winston Churchill's role in England during World War II?
    a. general   c. president
    b. prime minister   d. duke

_____ 7. What is the name given to the conflict between England's Royal Air Force and the German Luftwaffe?
    a. D-Day   c. V-J Day
    b. Battle of the Bulge   d. Battle of Britain

_____ 8. Who was the emperor of Japan during World War II?
    a. Hirohito   c. Mussolini
    b. Nagasaki   d. Yamamoto

_____ 9. What is the indigenous group in Japan?
    a. Haiku   c. Ainu
    b. Gigatu   d. Nippon

_____ 10. What is the meaning of Nihon, the Japanese name for their country?
    a. Red Sun   c. Land of the Sun
    b. Origin of the Sun   d. Rising Sun

Unit 25 Quiz

_____ 1. Who was the first leader of Soviet Russia?
  a. Lenin
  b. Stalin
  c. Khrushchev
  d. Trotsky

_____ 2. What was Churchill's phrase for the separation between free and Communist countries?
  a. Steel Curtain
  b. Iron Curtain
  c. Wall of Separation
  d. Berlin Wall

_____ 3. Where was the first major military confrontation between Communist and democratic countries in the early 1950s?
  a. Vietnam
  b. Cambodia
  c. Korea
  d. Japan

_____ 4. What country in Southeast Asia was a scene of fighting between Communist-led and American-backed forces in the 1960s?
  a. Cambodia
  b. Herzegovina
  c. Suriname
  d. Vietnam

_____ 5. What was _Sputnik_?
  a. the first space station
  b. the first rocket
  c. the first artificial satellite
  d. the first manned spacecraft

_____ 6. Who was the first person to orbit the earth?
  a. John Glenn
  b. Yuri Gagarin
  c. Alan Shepard
  d. Mikhail Baryshnikov

_____ 7. What was Ronald Reagan's first elected public office?
  a. President of the United States
  b. Senator from Illinois
  c. Senator from California
  d. Governor of California

_____ 8. To whom did Reagan issue the challenge, "Tear down this wall!"
  a. Gorbachev
  b. Stalin
  c. Khrushchev
  d. Putin

_____ 9. What kind of structures were promoted in the U.S. during the Cold War as offering protection from nuclear attack?
  a. coated umbrellas
  b. glass domes
  c. fallout shelters
  d. storm windows

_____ 10. What two kinds of state-owned farms existed in the Soviet Union?
  a. cattle and chicken
  b. collective and state
  c. local and national
  d. wealthy and poor

Fifth History Exam (Units 21-25)

1. Who became First Consul of France in 1802? _____

2. What empire experienced several revolts in 1848? _____

3. The Romanov dynasty ruled in what country from 1613 to 1917? _____

4. Guiseppe Garibaldi led a volunteer army called the Red Shirts in what country?

_____

5. At the height of its empire, what nation controlled one-fifth of the world's land area?

_____

6. What crop failed in Ireland in the mid-1800s and caused a severe famine? _____

7. In what country did George Müller care for thousands of orphans? _____

8. The first practical version of what invention was unveiled in England in 1829?

_____

9. Where was Karl Marx born? _____

10. Darwin admitted that a lack of what kind of evidence hurt his theory?

_____

11. Who was a pioneer in the field of psychoanalysis? _____

exam continued on the next page

12. Whose ethical philosophy developed into situation ethics?

_____

13. The assassination of whom triggered the start of World War I?

_____

14. What kind of government came to power in Russia during World War I?

_____

15. Which country helped rebuild Europe through the Marshall Plan?

_____

16. The Ainu is the indigenous group in what country? _____

17. Who was the first leader of Soviet Russia? _____

18. Who first used the phrase "Iron Curtain" referring to the separation between free and Communist countries?

_____

19. Yuri Gagarin was the first man to do what? _____

20. Who challenged Gorbachev to tear down the Berlin Wall? _____

Fifth English Exam (Units 21-25)

Match the writing on the left to the author on the right.

_____ 1. "Where Love Is, God Is"

a. Karl Marx and Friedrich Engels

_____ 2. "The Necklace"

b. John Dewey

_____ 3. *North and South*

c. Winston Churchill

_____ 4. Manifesto of the Communist Party

d. Guy de Maupassant

_____ 5. "The Man and His Newspaper"

e. Leo Tolstoy

_____ 6. *On the Origin of Species*

f. Corrie ten Boom

_____ 7. *Moral Principles in Education*

g. George Orwell

_____ 8. *The Hiding Place*

h. Charles Darwin

_____ 9. "The Sinews of Peace"

i. Elizabeth Gaskell

_____ 10. *Animal Farm*

j. G. K. Chesterton

exam continued on the next page

Match the parts of the plots on the left with the correct phrases on the right.

_____ 11. Mr. Thornton

_____ 12. Mr. Hale

_____ 13. Margaret

_____ 14. the SS guard

_____ 15. Beje

_____ 16. Corrie ten Boom

_____ 17. Napoleon

_____ 18. Boxer

_____ 19. windmill

_____ 20. indistinguishable

k. where Jews were hidden

l. the lead animal

m. met at a church meeting after the war

n. project undertaken by the animals

o. said "I will work harder"

p. told a lie about the train station

q. daughter of a watchmaker

r. factory owner close to his mother

s. had doubts about Anglican doctrine

t. what the animals and the humans became

Fifth Bible Exam (Units 21-25)

1. Who disguises himself as an angel of light? _____

2. Why is a mixed message a form of deception? _____

_____

3. When an elected official lies to the public, what does it say about his view of the public?

_____

_____

4. What is the proper response to God's kindness toward us?

_____

_____

5. What parable of Jesus teaches about being kind even when it is inconvenient?

_____

6. What did Rehoboam's older advisers say would happen if Rehoboam was kind to the people?

_____

7. What is the difference between textual criticism and higher criticism?

_____

_____

8. What is an assumption that higher critics make about the Bible?

_____

_____

9. How is true peace found?

_____

_____

exam continued on the next page

10. What is an amazing thing about peace within the fellowship?

_____

_____

11. Why is peace within the fellowship important to evangelism?

_____

_____

12. What are two ways that spiritual training is helpful?

_____

_____

13. What are the two images that Paul uses in 1 Timothy to describe fighting the good fight?

_____

14.-15. Write two paragraphs on how you believe the world could be a different place if more people had the peace of Christ in their hearts and were fighting the good fight instead of having worldly conflicts.

_____

_____

_____

_____

_____

_____

_____

_____

_____

_____

_____

_____

Unit 26 Quiz

_____ 1. A prominent dynasty in ancient China

a. Taiping

_____ 2. A mongol leader

b. Sultans

_____ 3. The name given to a Chinese rebellion that sought to restore Chinese traditions

c. Tokugawa

_____ 4. Leader of the Communist victory in China

d. Manchuria

_____ 5. Muslim rulers of India

e. Han

_____ 6. Leader of India's Congress Party after World War II

f. Meiji

_____ 7. Dynasty that ruled Japan from the 1600s to 1868

g. Genghis Khan

_____ 8. Japanese emperor who helped his country become modernized

h. Siam

_____ 9. Chinese province taken over by Japan prior to World War II

i. Mao Zedong

_____ 10. Uncolonized country in southeast Asia

j. Mohandas Gandhi

Unit 27 Quiz

_____ 1. Ethnic Spanish who were born in America were called:
    a. mestizos   c. peninsulares
    b. creoles   d. indigenes

_____ 2. Who was the leading figure in Latin American struggles for independence?
    a. Jose de San Martin   c. Toussaint L'Overture
    b. Simón Bolívar   d. Luis Aparicio

_____ 3. What United States policy warned European powers to stay away from Latin America?
    a. Monroe Doctrine   c. Big Stick Policy
    b. Good Neighbor Policy   d. Roosevelt Doctrine

_____ 4. The United States started developing a colonial empire as a result of what war?
    a. Civil War   c. Spanish-American War
    b. War of 1812   d. World War I

_____ 5. Who led Mexico during its conflicts with the U.S. during the early- to mid-1800s?
    a. Simón Bolívar   c. Austrian Maximilian
    b. Miguel Hidalgo   d. Santa Anna

_____ 6. The document that inflamed American opinion against Germany was the:
    a. Bismarck Concordat   c. Zimmerman Telegram
    b. Hindenberg Policy   d. North American Free Trade Agreement

_____ 7. Who was Jose de San Martin?
    a. the president of Mexico   c. a Cuban slave
    b. a South American freedom fighter   d. a descendant of German nobility

_____ 8. In what South American country is there an indigenous majority?
    a. Venezuela   c. Colombia
    b. Peru   d. Bolivia

_____ 9. What is the main indigenous language in South America?
    a. Chilean   c. Spanish
    b. Alpaca   d. Quechua

_____ 10. Religious beliefs in South America often contain a mixture of:
    a. native religion and Catholicism
    b. Spanish and Anglican teachings
    c. Baptist and Presbyterian doctrines
    d. American and Spanish beliefs

Unit 28 Quiz

Write a T if the statement is true and an F if the statement is false. If the statement is false, write a true version of the statement below it.

_____ 1. The Ottoman Empire took control of North Africa in the 1500s.

_____

_____

_____ 2. England once controlled more of West Africa than any other European nation.

_____

_____

_____ 3. Liberia was established as a home for freed slaves.

_____

_____

_____ 4. Ghana is the oldest independent nation in Africa.

_____

_____ 5. Spain invaded Ethiopia in 1935.

_____

_____ 6. Starvation killed about one million Ethiopians in the 1980s.

_____

_____

_____ 7. The Maasai live in Kenya and Tanzania.

_____

_____ 8. The Dutch established Cairo as a place for ships to rest on their way to the East Indies.

_____

_____

_____ 9. Boers were descendants of Dutch settlers.

_____

_____

_____ 10. Apartheid was the South African policy of immigration.

_____

_____

Unit 29 Quiz

_____ 1. Who built about fifty adding and subtracting machines in the 1640s?
    a. Johannes Gutenberg   c. Blaise Pascal
    b. Cecil John Rhodes   d. Charles Babbage

_____ 2. What was the first general purpose electronic computer called?
    a. ENIAC   c. ENIATO
    b. NATO   d. ECAIN

_____ 3. The push to create a Jewish state where Jews could live in peace was called:
    a. Freedom Fight   c. Zionist Movement
    b. Jewish Liberation   d. Quest for Peace

_____ 4. When was the modern state of Israel proclaimed?
    a. 1914   c. 1962
    b. 1948   d. 1989

_____ 5. What country gave up all its claims to the West Bank in 1988?
    a. Libya   c. Iraq
    b. Saudi Arabia   d. Jordan

_____ 6. What Middle Eastern country has the largest percentage of Christians?
    a. Israel   c. Lebanon
    b. Iran   d. Jordan

_____ 7. What country is the birthplace of Islam?
    a. Iraq   c. Afghanistan
    b. Saudi Arabia   d. Syria

_____ 8. Egypt, Syria, and Jordan joined forces to attack Israel in what is known as the:
    a. Six Day War   c. Thirty Days War
    b. Middle Eastern War   d. Arab War

_____ 9. What is the estimated number of homeschooled students in the United States?
    a. one to two million   c. 250,000
    b. four to five million   d. 100,000

_____ 10. What medieval pope reformed the calendar?
    a. John Paul   c. Benedict
    b. Alexander   d. Gregory

Unit 30 Quiz

Write at least one paragraph about why the study of world history is important.

_____

_____

_____

_____

_____

_____

_____

_____

_____

_____

_____

_____

_____

_____

_____

_____

_____

_____

_____

_____

_____

_____

_____

_____

_____

Sixth History Exam (Units 26-30)

1. Who was the leader of the Communist victory in China? _____

2. The Meiji dynasty ruled in what country? _____

3. Japan took over Manchuria in China prior to what war? _____

4. What country in southeast Asia has remained uncolonized? _____

5. Who was the leading figure in Latin American struggles for independence?

_____

6. Genghis Khan and Kublai Khan were leaders of what people? _____

7. Through the Monroe Doctrine the U.S. warned European powers to stay away from what?

_____

8. The Zimmerman Telegram was written by the foreign minister of what country?

_____

9. In what South American country is there an indigenous majority? _____

10. What empire took control of North Africa in the 1500s? _____

11. What nation once controlled more of West Africa than any other European nation?

_____

12. Liberia was established as a home for whom? _____

exam continued on the next page

13. Boers were descendants of what settlers?

_____

14. What is the oldest independent nation in Africa? _____

15. What is one country in which the Maasai live? _____

16. What was the name of the movement that sought to create a Jewish state?

_____

17. What Middle Eastern nation was established in 1948? _____

18. In 1988 Jordan gave up all its claims to what area? _____

19. Saudi Arabia is the birthplace of what religion? _____

20. If someone ever writes a lesson about you in a world history course, what are five things you would like the lesson to mention about your life?

_____

_____

_____

_____

_____

_____

_____

_____

Sixth English Exam (Units 26-30)

You may refer to the text of The Last Journals of David Livingstone (In Their Words, *pages 355-358)* *to help you in answering the following questions.*

1. What clues does the first entry give as to Livingstone's location?

_____

2. What did Livingstone add to the entry for 19th March that sets it apart from the other entries and shows his sincerity in writing that particular entry?

_____

3. Why is pride an obstacle to people being receptive to the gospel?

_____

_____

4. Why do you think Livingstone's journal is a mixture of important and mundane things? Give one example of each from these entries.

_____

_____

_____

_____

5. Why do you think music is an effective tool in evangelism?

_____

_____

_____

6. What was the English sailor communicating when he said, "If the devil don't catch these fellows, we might as well have no devil at all"?

_____

_____

_____

exam continued on the next page

7. What did the prince at Johanna say the unveiled faces of English women showed?

_____

_____

8. What does Livingstone say breaks down nationalities and brings geographically remote peoples into close connection with others?

_____

_____

9. What do you see as the benefits and detriments of those breakdowns?

_____

_____

_____

_____

10. Write a response to the statement: God surely is greater than His own laws.

_____

_____

_____

_____

_____

_____

_____

_____

_____

_____

_____

_____

Sixth Bible Exam (Units 26-30)

1. Write a paragraph on why it is important to help the poor.

_____

_____

_____

_____

_____

_____

_____

2. Write a paragraph on why it is important to be just.

_____

_____

_____

_____

_____

_____

_____

3. Write a paragraph on how a person should prepare for the end of the world.

_____

_____

_____

_____

_____

_____

_____